Also by Kirk Martin

Shade of the Maple

THE GRAVEL DRIVE

THE GRAVEL DRIVE

Kirk Martin

Cantwell-Hamilton Press

This book is a work of fiction. Names, characters, places and incidents are the product of the author's imagination or are used fictitiously. Any resemblance to actual events, locales, or persons, living or dead, is coincidental.

Please visit us on the web
www.kirkmartinbooks.com

Cantwell-Hamilton Press, LLC
1589 Skeet Club Road, Suite 102, PMB 351
High Point, North Carolina 27265

ISBN 0-9716145-1-2

Library of Congress Control Number: 2002093849

Jacket design and photographs by Julie Staton
Digital Artist, Steve Koger

Printed in the United States of America
10 9 8 7 6 5 4 3 2 1

To Casey

If I were the Creator,
and I could fashion a son with my own hands,
you would be my creation.

Children are the hands by which
we take hold of heaven.

- Henry Ward Beecher

Prologue

I have witnessed a thousand lifetimes through these panes of weary glass. Studied every stone toppled one upon another into shifting mounds, every stray branch crooked above our drive. I still say *our* drive, as if my boys are not gone, as if it remains *our* home.

I am a widow, but I am not old. Seems contradiction ruled our family. A homemaker who realized only late in life that it was not she that made this house a home, but the ceaseless chaos that scampered over the hardwood and echoed through splintered beams above. I just kept it neat. An advertising executive who spent his youth chasing the wind, only to discover the breath that gave lift to his wings lie softly in the bedroom down the hall. A little boy who grew up in Dixie craving the pastime of Canadians and cheering for Yankees.

A family defined by paradox, yet made stronger by it, somehow steeped in a simplicity that defied it. Playing together under the soft gaze of the North Carolina sky, a patch of heaven that shared its gentle shade of blue with no other. Resting under leafy Magnolias spotting the rolling lawns of Chapel Hill, strolling the bustling campus led by a panting Golden, combing the shops lining Franklin Street.

On summer weekends, we retreated two hours east to Wrightsville Beach, sea oats waving to us in the salty breeze. The boys valiantly fought waves as cresting mountains before surrendering to the late afternoon sun. Crisp autumn drafts carried us to the Blue Ridge Mountains boasting seas of color.

Our everyday retreat remained a small log cabin nestled in a stout patch of woods a stone's throw from town. A meandering road stretching from campus and courting tall shadows burrowed into our subdivision. A subdivision that welcomed the excesses of suburbia, Suburbans mortgaged against college plans, the present mortgaged against a future that would surely require no payment. Homes envisioned as sanctuaries had become nothing more than mirrors of the society families sought to escape.

Our cabin proved easy to find. Sweep down a sloping side street into a lonesome cul-de-sac, turn left at the portable basketball goal and up the gravel drive embraced by overgrown hardwoods and creeping blackberry bushes. My husband refused to even consider a blacktop entrance to his cabin—said "it would ruin the experience." Everything was about "the experience". Life was to be lived out in colorful scenes with bright blue skies and big yellow suns. Pictures you could simply draw yourself with crayons like an episode of Clifford the Big Red Dog.

He preferred a dirt entrance, all the more rustic, of course, until he *heard* the crunching of a gravel drive welcoming us home. And so gravel it was.

Southern pines and white and pink blooming crepe myrtles bordered the front and back yards, which stretched into a thicket of woods in either direction. A cracked slate walkway led past rhododendron and azaleas. Broad wooden steps welcomed guests to a front porch spotted with primitive rockers and hanging flowerpots.

Even frequent visitors couldn't resist pulling the cord to hear the painted woodpecker thump the pine door. The great room glowed with solace, its rough-hewn logs stretching to the heavens, reflecting the sun's golden blush. Somewhere beneath the beams on wide plank floors you would have found a little boy and grown man *acting like a little boy* wrestling and playing all manner of ball games.

That's what our house looked like to me. A house that became a home only after our son was born. A truth seared into our souls during a long summer that forever changed our lives, forever changed *us*.

A summer in which our little boy walked down that gravel drive and into the unknown.

Robby was a normal third-grader, a little boy with big dreams. Like all the other kids, but not really. He had a different sense about him, a certain contrary nature some would label difficult, others refreshingly unique. He was all boy, at once intensely intertwined in life and far removed from it. He rode his bike and scooter, played basketball and hockey, fought homework and sleep. Like every other kid, but not to us.

Somewhere in life's journey, little boys with big dreams become big boys with little dreams. And I'm not sure which dies first, the dream or the boy. I just know Robby never lost his sense of wonder.

We lived in a normal neighborhood, lived life like we were supposed to. We were active in Robby's school, gave him opportunities for camps and sports, a close family by all accounts. We envisioned that our little boy would grow up and go to college, play ice hockey for Boston College and ultimately pursue creative endeavors like his father. Ah, his father.

A skinny, fresh-faced college boy with boundless energy when I first met him. In him I saw the American Dream, a driven young man full of idealistic pictures of our life. And for the most part, those pictures developed as he had planned. But not without a price. He quickly rose through the ranks of a prominent advertising agency, transferring from city to city before settling in the heart of North Carolina, hours from his beloved Atlantic. He turned down offers with New York agencies luring him with prestige that had long since lost its appeal. Not that he had ever slowed down. He continued to work harder than others to maintain our "quality of life". He loved his little boy and I always thought him the ideal father. But that summer shook us, shook thoughts from him I never knew existed. Seems his drive was greater than his best intentions, larger than his heart.

It was a summer in which my husband could no longer paint the sky blue and hang a round yellow sun in the sky himself. A summer in which he no longer held the pen, couldn't write the ending to the story, couldn't paint the picture *he* wanted.

A summer when the illusion of perfection, like our hearts, was shattered into a million tiny pieces. When the world we had created became transparent and empty against reality, when scars showed strong against our son's innocence.

And during that summer, a story was written, one I had never known, because it had been written inside a man's heart.

Through this glass runs a wavy kaleidoscope of snapshots and grainy moving frames. If I look just right, I can see my own reflection. Like me, these windows caught the simple dance of leaves from naked limbs, unaware of the intricate web of life on a single, straggly pine. These windows were wakened by the soft light of the rising sun, felt its rage in July and craved its blanket in winter, but never understood how its sweep through the heavens altered the course of human life. These panes of glass revealed the world outside, but remained oblivious to the breath inside.

Profound thoughts you never quite grasp hold fast to the deep corners of a person's heart, even the man with whom you share a pillow and whose every pulse beats as your own.

I thought I knew this man and this little boy, thought I saw their story unfold through this window.

My eyes fill with their shadows moving slowly in the distance, hands clasped, off to discover another part of each other even they never knew existed. My heart longs to see them walking back up the gravel drive.

Until I peer into this tattered journal my husband left behind. A journal that tells the real story of that long summer when our sweet angel boy was taken from us.

A story of hope lost and hope regained, of second chances.

Journal - Day 1

1:34 am

Do you know the thoughts that crash like cruel waves through a father's mind while he crawls through woods to find his little boy? You consider all your failings, wondering why you didn't take more time, why everything else came before the most important people in your life. You wonder how you will live *without* your son when you didn't take the time to live *with* him when he was alive. You wonder if this is some strange retribution the cosmos brings upon you, a working of the universe to expose your hypocrisy, leaving you stripped bare like the naked moon that hangs in the sky tonight.

You wonder why everything you expressed and meant and felt never translated into actions, left for eternity as empty words that vanish as vapor. You are tempted to wonder why this had to happen to you, but you know better, that you deserved far worse, that you should have appreciated your son and treasured each moment when he was here.

You understand that time only moves forward and each second that is lost will never be regained. You learn that truth cuts deep, and without mercy.

Day 2

11:20 pm

Your little shadow lingered above the thirsty blades of grass at around 11:00 yesterday morning. I heard playful taunts and basketballs clanging off the stiff rim in the cul de sac thirty minutes later. That's when you called me to join your game, but I said, "Just a minute" and dashed inside to make a quick phone call.

When I returned, you were gone.

This is too hard. I'll have to finish later.

1:15 am

Brett and Daniel said they ran home for lunch at noon. You stayed out to play basketball. By yourself. Probably still waiting for me.

Two neighbors on Riverview Drive recall an unfamiliar dark minivan lurching through the neighborhood that morning. Said they thought a man was behind the wheel, possibly looking at houses for sale or taking a leisurely drive.

The police won't reveal the witnesses. I presume they don't want me involved, but I bet you one of them is Mrs. O'Grady. She never misses a thing through those musty drapes. Bad news for mischievous boys, but maybe she'll help find an innocent boy this time. Her roving eyes keep the neighborhood honest.

The police detailed the subdivision—a few neighbors own dark minivans, but none match the description. State Police are hunting for suspicious vehicles, though your captor could have changed cars or gone anywhere. You could be a mile from here, or far beyond our reach.

One witness swore it had North Carolina plates, the other can't recall. That's all we have. That and a prayer, which right now seems worthless.

Several neighbors have organized search teams with the police to comb the wooded areas in every direction. We have searched for two days straight, but haven't found any sign that you had trampled through the woods or fields.

All I found was an army hat and binoculars you had lost, back where I was going to build the fort for you. The one I never finished.

1:22 am

Shrill screams penetrate my bones like a January wind as I stagger from bed. I burst through the screen door, sinking slowly with each step into sodden earth, searching through blackness. Branches and thorns rip my shirt, soaked and pasted to my skin. I grasp blindly for your cries above pounding and gasps. Scratches and cuts become a certain consolation for the guilt and desperation inside.

Why does everyone remain asleep and blind to your voice? Even God seems uninterested in this search. Animals rustle through underbrush, scurrying as from a coming storm. My legs trudge through the uneven floor of brush and decay, the steady drone of insects drowning your faint whimpers. Gnats and mosquitoes swim in tiny pools of blood marking my arms and legs. Trees stand silhouetted in black against a cold, uncaring sky.

"Daddy! Daddy!"

Your fear swallows the thick night. My call of reassurance

is empty, and with every step I grow closer and yet further away. I try to catch my breath, listening for yours, desperately wanting to feel its warmth on my neck. The moon crashes through gray clouds and I see you move beyond a fallen pine. "Robby! Robby!"

Why are you running from me, why do you scamper deeper into darkness? It's me. Daddy.

I chase after you, but you run. Do you now hate me? Do you not trust your own father?

You turn. I see horror in eyes that reveal no soul, a hollow cavern, as if you no longer exist, a phantom taunting me. I grasp for your hand, your sweet face, the touch of your skin. I plunge into damp leaves and clutch you in my arms. You lie limp against my chest, a cold body without a soul, no breath warm against my cheek. I slowly move back and look right through you.

I cannot escape this nightmare whether I wake or sleep.

Day 3

12:45 pm

Two children have been abducted in eastern North Carolina and South Carolina since January. Neither has been found.

Who would take you, Robby? What could they want? I know what the statistics say—that it's most likely someone you know. Someone with whom you would feel comfortable, because you knew not to climb into a stranger's car. Unless you were forced.

Or somehow enticed into *helping* someone. Your most admirable trait, your most vulnerable weakness—an insatiable desire to help people.

Still, I cannot consider all the possibilities. I know what men do to little girls and boys.

7:10 pm

Strange the memories that prevail above this constant din of turmoil. On a majestic bluff high above Big Sur's pounding surf, I called to you. "Come on, boo-bear, let's go!" Your correction came innocently, yet without hesitation. "Daddy, I'm *Mommy's* boo-bear. I'm *your* peanut." Yes, we each have our affectionate names for you, which I learned you so comfortably wear.

2:25 am

The FBI asked me to compose a detailed description of you. Any distinguishing marks, the clothes you were wearing, mannerisms, speech patterns, anything that would aid in identification.

How do I begin? You are beautiful. Short brown hair that remains brushed for all of five minutes after a rare shower, blue eyes that match the sparkling waters of the Atlantic. A tiny indentation graces your left cheek, at the bottom of the smooth curvature. I see it when we are lying in bed talking or driving in the truck. Not sure why it's so meaningful, just something I like about you. Marble skin accented with a notch. Sometimes I cherish your flaws most—they make you unique, fully human and at the same time divine. Perfection is overrated.

You're no doubt wearing mismatched clothes with shirt untucked and socks pulled high above mud-covered sneakers. When you are excited, your face lights gorgeously and your eyes speak. I often find myself so lost in your animation that I don't hear what you say. When uncomfortable, even your statements sound like questions and you brush your fingers together nervously—occasionally we notice and you manage a sheepish grin, but you know we find it endearing.

A tattered and frayed Martin Brodeur hockey card rests in your pocket, your constant companion. Complete with our phone number scribbled on the back because you forget. Your mind always seems to be someplace else.

Remember that night in Toronto when Martin Brodeur responded to your timid wave with an affectionate wink through his goalie mask? You turned around as if you had seen Santa Claus. You are never without that card. I know your little hand and fingers are gripping it even now.

From the instant you wake imagining acrobatic saves to the moment you fall asleep clutching your favorite puck or jersey, hockey remains your passion. Only you could persuade me to spend spring break driving to Canada to purchase your first set of goalie pads—and then tucking each piece of equipment beside you in bed that night. I woke the next morning to streaks of early morning sun lighting a fully-clothed little goalie peering at me through his mask, ready to play a game of hotel room hockey.

Only lately have I realized that I have been fighting your very nature. You don't want to do things like everyone else—not teachers, not other kids, certainly not your parents. You know how you want to accomplish a task and nothing can persuade you otherwise. In fact, you seem to thrive on being different.

You are fiercely determined and sometimes beyond reach. But then you find yourself in a new situation and need my hand. I live for those moments even as I try to understand your contradictions.

It's only as I gaze into the mirror that I understand you.

Robby, I am falling in love with you all over again, enjoying you instead of trying to fit you into the mold of another's expectations.

I think the original mold is perfect.

You are beautiful.

Day 4

2:35 pm

A boy was seen struggling with a man outside a grocery store sixty miles to the south. We met the witnesses at the police station. Chills ran like a frozen river through my veins when the young couple described the boy. They spoke in raw adjectives about the color of his hair and his stature, but I felt your hand warm in mine, your heart pounding. The couple said the boy yanked his arm from the man's grasp and ran defiantly from the grocery store. The man caught the boy and pulled him through the parking lot.

It could have been a father and son, but their description makes me think it is you. He seemed to have a steady assurance, no fear of the man. That's why at first the couple didn't think the boy had been kidnapped.

I know you must be scared, Robby. But I know you are strong.

5:00 pm

I found the snowballs in the freezer today. The ones you gently placed in Ziploc bags last winter during our lone snow storm. You told Mommy you were saving them for a snowball fight in July with me. I promise I won't complain about the cold snow, about how illogical it is. And I will come when you call. We will have the best snowball fight ever.

8:15 pm

Detective McAllister asked me if repairmen, painters, or handymen have worked in our house lately—anyone who had access to you, a reason to take you. I couldn't recall anyone, only Mr. Melrose, the plumber, and we know him well. The detective asked me to find a record of everyone who has visited, from the UPS man to that crazy kid who delivers pizzas every other day. I bet he wonders where you are.

2:28 am

Who gave breath to this day, this week that has no end? You are still gone. Four days in which the hands of the clock never progress past midnight. Detectives McAllister and Graves instructed me to record my thoughts in this journal, hoping a stray memory will provide clues.

Guilt is my constant companion as I sit with pen in hand when I should be searching for you. Where are you, little boy?

The familiar crunching of the gravel beneath your feet grinds louder and louder in my head. I am haunted by the sound of your voice, the image of you walking away, a little boy with simple dreams and even simpler pleasures seeking his friends.

I can still feel the promise of that bright Sunday morning. Birds still sang and bees with no sting made honey. The screen door creaked and slammed behind you and by the time I looked up from wrestling weeds, you were bounding down the drive, hair and clothes tousled, teeth unbrushed I am certain, chores left for another time.

You walked away with a soft "Bye, Daddy" on your way to meet Brett and Daniel in the cul de sac. I was learning to adapt to your new freedom, but didn't always like it. I was no longer your sole playmate, though still your favorite. I knew a short time later, at the most inconvenient time, your plea to come play would cut through the noise of the day.

And so the giggling of three friends kept me company. Before long the pavement pounded with a steady thud of dribbling. The teams were chosen. As always. Everyone against me.

We never played the game. Other distractions called at the same time, their voices screaming with great urgency.

I want that moment back. I grasp for it, but it eludes me.

It was my fault, son. I am so sorry.

Day 5

11:15 am

Target called this morning, said our photos were ready. I was so hungry to see you, yet I dreaded walking into that store.

Every aisle wears vivid memories, a stage whose drama competed with Broadway. The gel pens you just have to have, or you will never be able to write another word. Searching for that special card for grandma, the "only good one" amongst the tens of thousands standing at attention. Trudging through household supplies, swearing you are too tired to take another step. Suddenly finding energy when toy cars and trucks play before your eyes. And you must have that one airplane or your entire fleet will be grounded.

Remember the time you and I played hide and seek from Mom. We disappeared down the candy aisle, of course, and I peeked around the corner. When I looked back at you, my eyes were lit with wonder. You begged me to tell you what I had seen. "Robby, I just saw the most beautiful girl in the whole wide world!"

You slowly moved to see for yourself. "That's not a girl. That's my Mommy and I'm going to marry her one day."

Good thing I beat you to her—she'd have taken you over me in a heartbeat.

Many nights we curled up in bed. You would look up at me, your soft skin and chubby cheeks and bright blue eyes glowing. You would point to a picture of Mom on your nightstand and ask in that slow, sweet drawl, "Is that the beautiful girl you saw in the store?"

I would brush your hair with my hand and pull you close. "Yeah. I'm really in love with her, too."

And you would ask, "Are you really in love with me, too, Daddy?"

And I don't know if you ever understood why my eyes were glassy, but I will never forget the way you nestled into my chest while I reassured, "Very much, so. Very much."

And now as I study every detail on your face and trace my fingers over these last images of you, I hurt and long for you. And I realize that pictures are all we have left.

4:55 pm

It's been five days and the police have no leads. I wonder if these cops know what they are doing, or just mimicking television detectives. Are they somehow recreating "Law and Order" in real life with Graves playing the tough guy, McAllister the reassuring cop?

McAllister *looks* like his name *sounds*. Big round guy whose gut appears to have been home to a few pints in his day. Always sweating, even inside. Seems like a kind man and I imagine he'd have a hearty, jovial laugh to share were circumstances different. He's been on the force eighteen years, which gives me some confidence. I don't ask too many questions about abductions because I can't bear the statistics. And I know it makes him uncomfortable.

Then there's Detective Graves. Comforting name for a man in his line of work. He wears a five o'clock shadow by the time he puts the razor down in the morning, short black hair, small but muscular build. A slight hitch accents each step, he's forever mumbling but seems somewhat studious. Never quite greets your eyes, always roving behind you, around you, like he's searching for clues in Monet's colors or wood stacked by the fireplace.

They ask a lot of questions, but I am anxious for answers.

11:48 pm

Why do I seek solace in this paper, as if you can hear me?

I should be crawling through woods, combing every inch of this state. But the FBI told me the best place for me is here, waiting for a call. What am I waiting for? A call from a kidnapper demanding something I cannot give? The police telling me they have found a body?

How can *they* find you when your mother and I know you best? Please forgive me, Robby. I want to be out there, I do. Please keep calling my name, and I will find you.

Day 6

2:00 pm

Two motels near the grocery store had record of men checking in late at night with young boys. Both men paid with cash, presumably under false names. Apparently not uncommon at such motels.

The FBI also found tire prints possibly matching those of the minivan in a dusty gas station lot nearby. They are checking receipts at businesses leading from the hotel.

It is torture to sit here waiting, wondering when the next call will come, and what news it will bring.

6:35 pm

Jimmy DeHart. That's whose name keeps coming to me. Three years ago, we renovated the house. DeHart was there day in and day out supervising the crew, but he often showed up "unfit" for the job. I told the general contractor about the problem, and he fired Jimmy. Swore he would get me one day, but I expected him to throw eggs at my house or slit my tires. Not take my son. This can't be anything, but I will tell Detective McAllister anyway.

12:45 am

Some TV Preacher. Claiming that God is a caring father who knows everything. And that God will save me.

From what? The hell I am living now. I do not sleep because nightmares haunt me more than waking thoughts. Besides, how can I sleep when I am certain you are lying awake somewhere terrified and lonely? I need to stay up with you, to let you know I am near.

If God knows everything, why doesn't He tell me where you are? How could He take my son from me?

And what does this preacher know? Begging for my money with no understanding of the torture that owns my soul.

2:20 am

It is so humid I feel like I am wearing the night. It sticks to me and you feel close by. I wandered through the neighborhood, hoping I could hear your voice in the stillness.

I walked by Mr. Holland's house, that creepy guy on Westridge. Every subdivision has one. The house that all the kids think is haunted, the ax murderer who never got caught. We had one up the street from us as kids, actually two.

One was Mr. Day. Ironic last name given he never stepped outside until nighttime. We would spy out our bedroom windows on late summer nights to catch him trudging to his beat up Volkswagen Bug. His driveway boasted nothing but cracked pavement, yet he never parked his car there. Always on the street. I guess that added to the mystique. But he was more creepy than scary, don't think he ever had the energy or desire to hurt anyone.

Mr. Lilly terrified us. Never thought about it until now, but his name bore no resemblance to his character, either. He was the spitting image of the old, bearded man in *Home Alone* with snow shovel and black boots. A big lumbering man who wore a black trench coat with a rough gray beard, menacing eyes and gruff voice. He walked with this long, exaggerated stride, sort of like Frankenstein. Thick weeds and tall grass dominated his yard, gobbling up our whiffle balls. We were too scared to rummage through the weeds, afraid we'd end up in the dungeon *we knew he had* in his basement. We learned later his wife had lung cancer. That's why his face wore a gloomy shadow. We never know another's torment.

I'll ask Detective Graves to run a background check on Holland. I can't bring myself to use the "m" word, but I hope one of *those* hasn't been released into our neighborhood.

Day 7

10:45 am

Damn cops. What do they know? Suddenly swarming all over the house, questioning us like we had something to do with this. Why would we hurt our own son? Guess they aren't good enough to find the real suspect so they turn the focus to us. Graves hobbles around the house, like *he* could ever track someone down. Just mumbles and asks strange questions, nods and says, "Uh huh." Guess he's friendly enough, but he unnerves me.

They even harassed your Mom, and it was too much for her to bear. She kept muttering through tears, "Why would I hurt my son? Please find my son. Please find my son." I demanded they leave. From now on, they only talk to me.

They searched the house, every bit of it. Do you know how humiliating that is? To watch police officers searching for the evidence to prove you hurt your own son. I asked

Detective *Graveyard* why he wasn't searching Holland's house like this.

Their questions assault a mind already saddled with guilt and confusion, tempting me to doubt my own innocence. I first recall going inside at 11:30, but then remember that the top of the hour newscast was playing on the radio so it was really 12:02. And so that becomes some sort of pathetic evidence that I was lying. I haven't been able to think straight for the past week, but then I am interrogated and asked to remember every detail of a seemingly insignificant summer morning. They want specific times, but I'm lucky if I know the day of the week. I fear that calling my attorney and repeating, "I don't recall" will create the impression I am trying to hide something.

And so the circus winds to full chorus, news trucks are camped out front and everything in our lives becomes fair game. My speeding tickets, the job I lost, the time a neighbor heard us having an argument, the time I barreled out of the driveway. They will piece together six insignificant events to indicate a pattern, and before long Mom and I are prime suspects.

The danger is allowing the focus to be taken off the real suspect, who with each passing moment has another opportunity to hurt you. So I cooperate in order to speed them along and return their focus outward.

All we want is our son.

4:25 pm

The FBI has ruled out any link to the recent abductions. In both cases, teenage girls disappeared in large crowds. They will keep tabs on those investigations, but don't consider it worth diverting resources to pursue further.

11:55 pm

I sit alone again tonight, feet dangling above this irritable lake slapping against splintered docks. I want to slip into the water and become one with the darkness I know so well. It can swallow me without noticing and perhaps swallow my pain and hollowness. I feel my body slump and hips give out, my legs plunging toward the blackness. Frail arms lower me until I am inches from letting go. Water splashes my legs and draws me deeper.

I want to let go, Robby. This pain is too great, it is making me crazy. I never knew the human heart could absorb so much pain, never knew the mind could be imprisoned so sternly to such fears. I've always been in control. But this is beating me. I feel the current tug on my torso, begging me to let go, wanting to engulf me in its silent vengeance. But if I let go, then I am a coward and not fit to be your father. I will wait for you, Robby. I will wait.

I can only imagine the fear and utter horror in your eyes. You are screaming for me. Who is this man, Daddy? Where am I? Why did he take me? Why aren't you here? Where is Mommy? Will I ever see you again?

Do you fill your days thinking these questions? Does your heart feel abandoned? You don't have your asthma medicine. Can you breathe okay, Robby? What if something happens and you have an attack, what will you do? I hate him.

I try to picture the sky and trees and sun, but a little face filled with dread and terror burns in my eyes. Nothing I do can make it disappear.

I swear I will kill him, whoever took you. If he so much as lays a finger on you, I will tear his body apart piece by piece. I will make sure he never does this again. And I will make him feel the anguish he has caused you. No one who hurts the innocent deserves mercy.

I see your eyes staring back at me on flyers posted all over town and cannot escape. I don't want to see you relegated to a missing face on a milk carton.

Day 8

12:25 pm

No stained glass windows. No huge cross above the altar. Sure didn't seem like a church, more like an auditorium. Your mother dragged me there.

Not sure why she thinks this will help. Why do these people pray to a God who doesn't hear a father's cry for his son? What could they possibly be praying for that compares to you?

The Preacher spoke for what seemed an eternity, but everything became muffled after I heard one sentence.

"All children go to Heaven when they die."

I'm sorry, Robby, I didn't mean to imply that I think you're dead. A week has passed, and I don't know what to think. But if you have been taken from us, then I guess there is some consolation in believing you are in heaven. But I am not sure I ever believed in a heaven or hell. Doesn't make sense to me why God would create people and then banish some to eternal doom and welcome others to paradise. We're all pretty much the same so far as I can see, separated only by degrees of kindness. Except for your mother. If there are saints, then she is one. The way I see it, she has suffered her hell here so paradise must be imminent for her.

But the guy who took you deserves eternal hell and the sooner he begins his sentence the better.

I would be inclined to believe in heaven if pictures of you peaceful and content will replace these dreadful images. Perhaps that is why Mom comes to church. Still unnerves me to be in this place, feels like I am in a different country. I gaze at these people and some of them glow like the sun has set upon them.

5:15 pm

There used to be rules to life, everything so prescribed. I knew how to act no matter the situation. Knew how to be the wise businessman entertaining clients, the respectful gentlemen in social circles, the happy-go-lucky guy with friends. But now there is no order, there are no rules.

Will I ever laugh again? My son is missing and were I to smile, that would be unseemly. How are people supposed to act around me?

I want to help your Mom escape this hell for a few minutes. But what kind of movie do I choose? We need a lighthearted moment to soothe the grim faces that stare back in the mirror. But could I really rent a comedy? We are living a far worse horror or drama than Hollywood could produce.

This nightmare has become my habitation.

10:45 pm

I am angry. Angry at the cops, angry at God, angry at your mother, angry at myself. Not sure why. Maybe it's a way to cope. I never knew hatred could consume a person like this. I fear if I let it go, it will mean I have somehow stopped caring for you. I hate the person who took you, want to torture him one day for the pain and anguish he has caused our family.

1:00 am

It is cold and black and heavy. Shines in the moonlight. I feel the power in my hands and I shiver. The power to take life, to exact revenge and execute justice. My thumb holds fast against the handle and my finger slowly pulls the trigger. Done. In an instant, an eye for an eye. The power of God resting in my palm.

I roll six bullets between my fingers, feeling the sharp points that will pierce his flesh and puncture his heart. He will lie dead and shaking in a pool of his own cold blood.

I load death into the chamber and tell myself there is no mercy for someone who harms an innocent child.

I owe it to you to cause him pain, to see the horror in his eyes that must be in yours, when the heavy black barrel is inches from his face.

Day 9

11:35 am

A convicted child molester named Roger Spivey lives in Cowpens Mills subdivision next to ours. Great. You boys ride your bikes over there all the time. That's where Daniel lives.

Holland is squeaky clean, guess he's just an odd man. Evidently, Spivey was convicted and sentenced to fifteen years behind bars for sexually assaulting two young boys. But his conviction was overturned a year later on a legal technicality. So some lawyer without a soul discredits the anguish of two little boys and a predator roams our streets. I cannot believe they allow a child molester to move into a subdivision teeming with kids without notifying parents.

Screw his rights. If someone hurts a child, they lose their rights. Graves and McAllister had to restrain me from rushing to Spivey's house. He could have you in his house right now and no one would know. McAllister assured me they are verifying his story. It better not be him. Anyone but him.

2:20 pm

A tender breeze cools my face, baked by a sun that seems to hang at high noon for hours. We would be playing outside today. Mr. Henson has been giving his lawn a manicure since daybreak. He's retired so I guess it's part excuse to stay busy, part excuse to stay out of the house and preserve the good marriage he and Mrs. Henson enjoy.

He always asks if he can help me with *our* yard. It is marred with divots and barren patches and matted grass where we played soccer endlessly last fall. The imaginary goal you shot toward spread the width of the garage. My goal, of course, could be measured in inches and somehow found itself smaller as each game progressed.

I watched week after week as thick green grass gave way to

dirt. The patches spread like a quilt, transformed from oasis to desert. I sowed seed so we could have fresh grass to trample this summer.

But I do not want it to grow, Robby. I want to keep my backyard like it is. It is your playground.

11:30 pm

I wandered into your room today. Just sat on the bed and cried. I grasped your quilt and buried my head in your pillow, your smell was there and I could feel you. I saw your little sneakers, your books, your dinosaurs and your hockey pucks all lined up in a row. And a lone pair of shorts in your hamper. You couldn't have put them there, you preferred the floor.

I picked up the shorts, stared at the grass and dirt stains, emptied your pockets. A small stone you would have added to your collection. No reason in particular, just because you wanted to keep it. The crushed stem of a dandelion ground into sinewy threads. Another flower you had picked for Mom but forgotten to give to her.

A week ago Saturday, you stood in the yard talking to Mom while I had my head buried in work on the front porch. It was "yellow" outside, as you called daytime. A quiet breeze played in your hair and the sun was made brighter by your eyes. You held the dandelion to your nose and then blew. Mommy asked what you wished for.

Could have been anything in the world. A new car or truck, but you didn't much care for things.

So what did you wish for, little boy? Whisper it again to me. Let me hear your voice, just one more time. This time I will come.

"That Daddy would play with me."

4:30 am

I woke to the worst nightmare yet.

You were dead. Dead.

We were too late, Robby.

I put your hand in mine, felt your fingers cold and limp. I clutched you, grasping for one last hug, yet your heart did not beat. You would never wrap your warm little fingers around mine and walk carefree in the sand. Your voice would never sing to us again, your face never be as sunshine, nor your eyes as rain.

You would never gaze into my eyes and call me, "Daddy."

The salt from my tears tried in vain to breathe life into you, but you lie still. I sobbed and touched your skin, stroked your hair. Like I used to in bed before you fell asleep.

I saw that little indentation on your cheek, even in my dream.

I never realized how beautiful and perfect you are.

Day 10

10:25 am

A man from Greenville, South Carolina reported a reckless driver barreling through a red light, in a van matching the description. Police say the caller indicated it was a man with a young boy. Didn't get the tag number, though he said it had North Carolina plates. The FBI has swarmed the area, hungry for fresh clues.

2:00 pm

Sun splashes through the windows lighting the World Trade Center Towers you built several days after they fell. I remember peeking into your bedroom to watch you playing. You were carefully constructing your own twin towers, topped with an American flag made of red, white and blue Legos. I was stunned by its beauty. But then I spotted an airplane nearby and thought you were going to crash it into the towers, Legos tumbling, as little boys sometimes do.

Instead, you held the towers reverently and examined them, making sure they were perfect. You caught me out of the corner of your eye and without blinking asked, “Daddy, can we glue these together so that they never fall?”

My heart caught in my throat. A few months prior to the attack, we had gazed at the New York City skyline from a darkened hotel room across the Hudson. I knew the Towers and the city held special meaning to you. But your reverence for the people, the Towers and the American flag—wanting to preserve them all as if September 11th had never happened—moved me.

You should have seen the sunrise greet the flag this morning. I tried to draw strength from the resolve those colors represent, defiance in the face of evil, hope and courage amidst despair. I remember peering out the window last fall, and there you were in your camouflage uniform, saluting the flag. An innocent little boy expressing a truth he knew inside but couldn’t explain.

It was always in unspoken acts that you said the most about yourself. These towers will never fall, I promise. And this flag will be waving to greet you when you come walking back up the gravel drive.

5:30 pm

They can't find DeHart. Anywhere. The lousy, disgruntled painter who couldn't leave the bottle long enough to do his job.

His landlord said he skipped out of his apartment last month without warning. Lost his job and had been unable to find work.

The FBI and police are scouring hotels near the other sightings for positive identification. The previous witnesses did not recognize his picture, but police will follow the leads regardless.

11:40 pm

So which father do you think of now? I curse under my breath at my failures, but I do not sulk in anger at the situation. My hatred is turned inward for I fear I have filled your heart and mind with far too many pictures of me as an evil man instead of a good one. The truth is that I am both, but a young boy should not have to weigh the balance in his own father.

What images fill your mind as you lie there alone? The days we rode in the truck and talked about everything under the sun? The times we celebrated your victories and played together? Or the times when I ceased to be man enough to be your father and in some perverse nod to my own lack grew competitive in sport, frustrating you. And in that lack I realize I am a shallow and hollow man. Without you, I am made even more so, til I am no man at all.

It is only in you that I grew into something to be proud of, and yet I continued to disappoint. I walked away from a fight not mad at you, but ashamed of the person I am, afraid that you will grow up haunted by the same demons I have yet to overcome.

I lie ashamed. Like a worm slinking in the dirt, trying to hide behind a rotted blade of grass, squirming for cover under a rock. I wear shame in my eyes and I see it for what it is—not just a human frailty. I see selfishness. And I hope that is not the father you remember.

Because all too often that is the real one. And I dread the thought of you replaying your short life in your mind somewhere, wondering why your father has not come to find you. These are thoughts your mother does not understand. She is pure of heart, and only asks the unanswerable questions. But she doesn't understand how the sins of a father are passed to his child without mercy, and how truly weak I am. I have chosen a selfish path too often, trying to somehow balance the good and evil within so that good maintains a slight edge.

Not considering that even a whisper of evil has consequences, and that my life will not be weighed on a scale of simple majority.

I fear that you fall asleep at night with images of me responding angrily to you or fighting over insignificant matters, allowing a bad mood or weariness to excuse harsh words. I have had you for eight short years, and the thought that I have wasted even a moment with petty selfishness is a heavy burden.

Please give me another chance.

2:22 am

I can't sleep again tonight, can't escape this question that keeps rolling through the caverns of my heart like thunder on a summer afternoon.

If you are there, in heaven, I want to be there, too. If I can't see you on earth, I have to be with you forever.

Will I be there?

Day 11

9:15 am

It's there. Clear as day. Captured on film. A picture of that dark mini-van speeding through the intersection with North Carolina license plate framed perfectly in the middle. The camera did its job.

Roadblocks crisscross the highways while choppers pursue above. The detectives warn that this guy could be many states away or have changed vehicles by now. We decided not to release specific information to the media. The FBI knows the suspect will use information from radio and TV broadcasts. If he knows we have identified his vehicle, he'll ditch it. So it remains a matter of balancing the need to use the public as eyes and ears and arming the suspect with information he could use against us. The strategy is to lull the suspect into a false sense of security, waiting for him to make a mistake.

Funny how perspective changes when *your* son is missing.

You don't mind nosey neighbors or media vultures, and you're willing to dismiss personal privacy rights, whether it's a camera capturing your car on film or law enforcement investigating suspects.

All you care about is being with your child again, everything else be damned. Maybe that's how I should look at life all the time.

12:05 pm

The sun is hanging high in the sky today, the kind of day you loved to be outside.

Brett's father is still on his mower. Wearing khaki shorts and black dress socks. I promise I'll never do that to you, Robby. Must be trimming his lawn one blade at a time. Think it's because he can't stand to be stuck inside with Mrs. Russell? I know that's a mean thing to say, but she is one cantankerous woman. I just heard your voice asking, "Daddy, what is cantankerous?"

Your buddy Taylor is at his grandma's house next door. I hope he doesn't come over. I don't have the heart to tell him you aren't home—it makes his eyes sad. He's walking through the brush of thin woods between the houses now. His little legs shuffle through dry leaves, arms shoving branches out of the way. I can see him, but I don't look up yet. The sun is lighting his face and he cups his hands around his eyes, approaching the front porch.

"Hi Taylor. How are you today, little guy?"

"Good. Can Robby play kickball with me?"

"Taylor, Robby's not home right now. Sorry."

"When will he be home?"

"I'm not sure."

11:55 pm

Spivey's sick face covered newscasts tonight. They are reporting he is not a suspect. How can he not be a suspect? He's a convicted child molester living less than a mile from the home of a missing child. What are they thinking? Why am I getting updates from the media and not from the police?

I woke Detective Graves, but didn't feel any guilt for the disturbance. He explained that if they arrest and formally charge Spivey now, it limits their ability to gather evidence and grants him protective rights. Graves assured me that they are examining his every move. At least they have exposed him. I hope it chases him from this area, even if he didn't do it.

1:00 am

I miss your little boy smell, a messy house and peanut butter spread across the counter as if it were bread. I miss emptying your pockets and finding stones and bugs and the flower you picked for Mom but forgot to give her. I miss you falling asleep in the car and carrying you up to your room, your head on my shoulder, drooling on my shirt, changing you into your pajamas, watching you absorbed into the comfort of your bed, turning on your side and curling up while muttering.

I miss you clutching Mr. Bear, your fierce independence surrendering to complete dependence.

Day 12

10:45 pm

We found a body.

McAllister's words stunned me. A construction worker discovered a child's body in an abandoned building in Columbia, South Carolina. We won't be able to make the identification for a few hours. I've never felt my hands shake like this, never felt my stomach churn as if someone dumped acid straight into my gut. I don't know how to tell your Mom. I don't know what to think, you have to forgive me, I have so many thoughts colliding in my head.

I know this isn't going to sound right, but part of me wants the body to be yours. So I can see your sweet face and touch your little hands again. I miss you so much, Robby. And part of me selfishly wants this to be over, to have some measure of closure. It's *not* knowing that torments us, wondering with each tick of the second hand where you are, imagining the pain and desperation you must feel. Death would bring you peace.

But I never want to say, "My son is dead." As long as you are alive, there is hope I will see you again, even if it means you remain vulnerable. I don't know what to think. Is it right to hope the body is someone else's son?

12:20 am

A penetrating chill has swept the countryside. Stars flicker against a canvas of midnight blue. The moon seems oddly alone, yearning for clouds to keep it company. It casts a strange, hollow glow.

I am afraid. When I walk into that cold, sterile room and pull back the sheet, I fear I will see the hope and promise of a little boy ground into the desolation of his father's failures.

Day 13

4:10 am

It wasn't you. You are still out there, Robby. Send a whisper on this breeze, draw me to you.

I am haunted by the little boy. He could have been you. Sweet. Innocent. If the preacher is right, he is in heaven now. And a father and mother have lost their little boy. God help them.

12:35 pm

The sun rose with a vengeance today, white-hot, blistering everything in its grasp. I do not know how to recover from last night. I see you in the little boy's face and delicate body.

Your mother has gazed out the window since daybreak, waiting for you. She stands there for hours on end, and nothing I say can comfort her. She made lemonade in a big pitcher, to alleviate the heat. Neither of us drink lemonade.

2:15 am

My hands tremble. Shards of glass and jagged cubes jut from thick pools on the floor like icebergs. I touched the bottle, felt the cool, smooth glass. My fingers traced over the label, up to the short neck. I started to pour until I saw a million tiny demons lurking and slithering around the lip, taunting and begging me. Every ounce of me pleaded for a lone slip, just one, I swear it would be just one.

But I had heard myself say that too many times before.

Day 14

12:50 pm

Guess who stopped by? Officer Bill and a firefighter buddy named Jackson. One of the few people I want to see. Somehow they know how to mix the right balance of humor and concern. Maybe because they face suffering every day.

Officer Bill asked if he could see your bedroom. He saw the police cap hanging on your bedpost. Bill gave you his that night he was patrolling the office because he thought you were a special kid. He patted the cap as if it were on your head and looked away. You've got a good friend on your side.

Jackson brought you a firefighter's helmet. He asked if you would mind that it bears the scars of fires. I told him you'd like that better than a new one. He had thought so, too.

So then he and Bill began arguing over which hat you'd like better, the police cap or firefighter's helmet. I stayed out of it. Never realized how competitive these guys are. Jackson started in on Bill with the usual donut jokes. Bill countered that he failed out of firefighter school because he couldn't meet the primary requirement—cooking gourmet meals. So he decided to earn a *real* living. Jackson asked why cops thought it necessary to prevent crime only around donut shops. Bill said he sees more firefighters in grocery stores planning meals than putting out fires. Their banter continued, but I sense they share mutual respect. They are real men, men whose depth is often hidden.

I smiled and laughed for a few minutes. But I cannot escape the weight worn so sternly upon my heart, an unending weeping inside.

2:35 pm

The van was purchased from a run-down, roadside car dealer/service shop along the Virginia-North Carolina border with cash three days before you were taken. Probably the kind of place draped in red, white and blue streamers left over from Bicentennial celebrations twenty-five years ago with a handwritten sign over the trailer door reading, "Bad Credit, No Problem!"

The FBI is checking its databases to determine if the registered owner, James Anderson, is an alias. The police are puzzled why the van was purchased north of here.

6:20 pm

I can't believe this television report. Great, another neighbor telling us what a *nice guy* he seemed to be. He is a child molester! What do you mean Spivey was *acting strange* around the time my son disappeared? Of course he acts strange. It's his nature. Those guys are never cured. It's just a matter of time before they hurt another child.

And now a report indicates that thousands of convicted child molesters have violated their agreements by failing to register with the state upon moving. Which ultimately means that officials are clueless about where these predators are living. Most states barely have an active registry in place. These sick animals need to be locked away for good, delivered to other prisoners for just retribution. How can anyone defend a monster that preys on innocent children?

It demands all my resolve to keep from busting Spivey's door down to search for any sign of you. I want to strangle his sick neck until he tells me where you are. He deserves no better. The police assure me they will find out what he was doing exactly two weeks ago, but do I want to know?

8:15 pm

Jimmy DeHart has bounced from place to place, looking for work. Detective Graves said he's difficult to track—an all cash guy, no bank account, nothing permanent.

Fate has delivered to me the abhorrent position of weighing which captor I *hope* has taken you. I cannot allow the possibility that a child molester has you. I vomit from such thoughts in the middle of the night. I wretch violently until the sobbing makes it stop. Your mother tries to calm me but I cannot wrestle the images free.

Other parents are planning vacations. I am hoping my son has been taken by accident, or taken for ransom. At least a greedy man would not harm you because he needs you. I would steal, I would run up my credit limit, anything to get the money for you. I want that chance, to have you safe again.

What would some lazy, disgruntled painter want with you anyway? Who has you?

10:45 pm

We lumbered through the grocery store this evening, searching for *anything* appealing. Your fingers weren't wrapped around my belt loops. You weren't scurrying ahead to the toy section for a three-dollar car. You weren't tugging me from the book section. I didn't get in trouble with Mom for charging down the aisles with you grasping the cart for dear life.

We reached the register far too quickly, with nothing fun in the cart. No orange and purple and green boxes with free prizes inside. Nothing loaded with sugar. No popsicles for summer afternoons. Just boring grown-up food, none of which we can find a taste for anymore.

We need our little boy back.

Day 15

12:30 pm

Would you be proud of me if I told you I spoke with the Preacher today? I've never done that. Never had much use for those guys, always equated them with ad guys like me. Selling you something big that's never as good as they claim.

I thought your Mom was going to faint when I took the first step toward him. I introduced myself, but didn't tell him about you. He gripped my hand and peered into my eyes. I saw compassion in his. I wonder what he saw in mine.

I asked him about heaven and hell, about where kids go when they die. He promptly asked me to his office. Maybe he knew what I was really asking, I don't know, maybe he does have some connection to the Almighty.

He explained it this way. He said that heaven and hell are merely eternal extensions of what you have experienced on earth. If you have a relationship with God here, that will continue throughout eternity. That's what Heaven is—an eternal relationship with God. But if you have not had a relationship with God on earth, then in his estimation you are already living a kind of hell and that merely continues into eternity. He equates separation from God with hell. I guess I understand in terms of missing you—being apart from you is hell.

I know I want to be with *you* forever, but I am not sure about a relationship with God. I am not one for doing what others want me to do. I've always done it on my own, you know.

2:30 pm

It feels like spring outside. I feel cold and dead inside.

Long shadows clothe the mound of leaves you raked last fall on the side of the house. I can still hear the giggles of little boys jumping and splashing in the pile. We never picked the leaves up or swept them into the woods. And now the grass is dead there.

I cherish my pile of leaves and brown clumps of grass. You jumped and fell and screamed and giggled there.

5:45 pm

He's lying. Spivey. That sick bastard. I want him to be innocent, let it be anyone but him. He originally told police he had been at work the Friday before you were taken and home that weekend, including the Sunday you disappeared. His employer confirmed he was at work that Friday, but had left early and clocked in late Monday morning. Credit card receipts showed he purchased heavy trash bags and a shovel from a local Home Depot Friday night, and gas two hours south in Charlotte on Sunday night. Which puts him in the suspected path of the van. They are searching his house. Please don't let them find other little boys. Let the search be futile.

8:00 pm

The police found the van. Hidden in a field behind a crumbled old brick cellar covered with brambles and overgrown weeds.

It had been cleaned up. No traces of blood, no signs of struggle, nothing out of the ordinary. Just some crumbs in the backseat.

And a single hair.

Perhaps it is yours. I am so desperate, Robby. I want to see your hair again, want to know it is you, that you are still alive. I want to believe this is a mistake, that he took you by accident, that he isn't touching you.

The FBI is reviewing surveillance tapes at convenience stores, trying to piece together a timeline of the suspect's activities. The police are scouring the area for any sign of you. Was it Spivey? DeHart? Someone else?

It's been over two weeks and we still don't have a solid clue where you are or who took you. It can't be for ransom. We would have received a call by now. And the detectives ruled out any link to recent kidnappings. So we are left with someone in a van headed south, Spivey and a lousy painter who can't keep a job because the bottle owns him. How long will this continue?

1:45 am

I miss you so much, Robby.

Day 16

12:35 pm

We heard you. The gravel crunches and our hearts race into our throats. Mom and I sit with faces blank against a television screen. You turn the doorknob, slowly.

I turn, unable to utter a word. I stare without blinking so you won't disappear. I rise slowly and make my way to you, never taking my eyes from yours. I reach out and touch your skin. Your hands are dirty and sticky and grimy. But warm. Your skin was always warm. I never touched you when your skin was not warm. I breathe in your little boy smell. A mix of grass and leaves and dirty basketballs and sweat. You are fragrant.

I don't want you to clean up, don't want you to shower. I want you to sit next to me with your hand on my knee and watch basketball. When I ask you to go to bed, I want you to stall and ask for one more minute.

I want that one minute to stretch into five minutes, to ten, to eternity.

I want you to ride with me in the truck and ask countless questions. I want to hear your giggle, I want to see you asleep in bed grasping your bear.

You are warm. You are alive. You are mine again. I am whole.

Were it possible by sheer determination and desire to make you walk up the driveway, you would be sitting next to me now. My only consolation is this daydream.

I would forfeit my life to return yours. You have so much to give, so much to learn and explore. I have already had a good life. But it ended sixteen days ago.

3:00 pm

DeHart is a low-grade criminal. Apparently so lazy he couldn't find the energy to commit worthy crimes. Nothing but a rap sheet littered with misdemeanors. Disorderly conduct. Petty larceny. Theft. Aggravated assault. Such a reassuring thought to know he was in our house every day.

Georgia police pulled him over for speeding two weeks ago. Had an expired license from the State of North Carolina. Imagine that.

I don't understand why he would take you. Then again, I don't understand why anyone would harm a child. Would he really carry a grudge for three years? Could getting fired from Donald Lufkin's crew have blackballed him from construction crews in the area? I don't know.

1:15 am

The night is thick and I feel you in my bones. Your fingers wrap around mine and we sit quietly.

What I would give for a moment with you, a moment to absorb you. So many minutes, hours, days I wasted, lured by other passions, distracted by empty promises.

I was selling a new ad campaign, planning a trip, calling my broker. I was wondering who was winning the big game, developing marketing strategies to sell products and win awards.

I was there with you, playing the role of the good father. Wrestling on the floor, playing catch in the backyard, running beside you while you learned to ride your bike, walking hand in hand to the store for a slurpee. But I wasn't really present. I was acting out a role I was supposed to play. I didn't feel it, it didn't move me.

Now that time is lost, never to be regained. And what do I

have to show for it? So I increased sales or built awareness of a new product. Try weighing that in the balance of eternity versus time focused on you.

This must be a nightmare, Robby, it can't be real. You can't be gone. We have a perfect life here, it has to be someone else. Please tell me it isn't you that they have. Please come back and let's start over again.

I want another chance, a chance to make the right choices, to choose you and Mom instead of my pursuits.

I want your voice whispering in my ear, your breath warm against my cheek, little fingers wrapped around my hand. I want to grasp the beauty of your soul in those wondering blue eyes, understand the largeness of your heart beating beneath your smooth, soft skin.

I want to know you in the smallest of ways.

Day 17

12:30 pm

Spivey claims he attended a convention in South Carolina the weekend you were abducted. Great, probably a pedophilia convention. So why did he lie about being home all weekend? What is he trying to cover up?

They are searching his computer for improper contact with children on the Internet. All I know is that he lied, he had access to you and he was in South Carolina, where the van was last seen.

2:20 pm

The only thing I want is you, Robby. I want to hear you call my name. I want to feel your clammy little fingers folded into mine and your head buried into my shoulder seeking warmth. I want to see the house a mess.

Your Mom and I looked forward to the day when

everything would be in its place, everything in order, just so.

Clean. Neat. Miserable.

We longed for days that sang with peace and quiet, when we could talk to each other uninterrupted.

Now the silence bleeds.

6:10 pm

A young boy was with DeHart. The Georgia State Police Officer who ticketed DeHart also reported that he was driving a late model Ford Taurus. They are tracking the plates, crosschecking the database.

11:45 pm

It was your hair. It *is* your hair.

You were there. The police collected a sample of hair from your pillow and matched it against the little strand of hair from the abandoned van. They tell me the test is not conclusive, but I know it is yours.

Why is it you stood before me so many days and I failed to hug you, to muss your hair with affection, to simply touch your skin? And now I am humbled and broken by the sight of a single strand of your hair?

2:25 am

I was only 17. I didn't know what I was doing. It was an ordinary Friday night. Went to a party with friends, hung out and drank a few beers. I don't even remember grabbing the keys, just waking up in a daze to lights flashing, men yelling, people in white and blue shirts tearing my clothes and bandaging me.

I remember them lifting me onto a hard board and wheeling me on a stretcher.

Then time stood still, everything moved in slow motion. The lights piercing the night sky, commotion all around, while I turned my head and saw a sheet lying over a little body on the road, head covered.

I didn't mean to do it, you know. How could I have known?

Day 18

12:10 pm

They found pornography. Child pornography. In the dump with trash from his apartment complex. In a large plastic bag, lined twice. They wouldn't have known except for a small catalog with a mailing label still attached. No, not Spivey. James W. DeHart II. The more refined version of the sick man. He left his apartment spotless, without a speck of dust. But he didn't count on the cops digging through the dump.

Dirty, filthy animal. Little boys and girls. I cannot even think about it.

7:25 pm

I went back to work today. Walked down hallways that seemed narrow and stale. Climbed into a chair that used to be my home. Now it feels empty and oddly unsatisfying, like everything without you. How many minutes and hours and days did I spend laboring over a tiny detail from the office when something so magnificent waited for me at home? What means more, an idea to be created or a life to be shaped?

I am torn. Should I go back to work? I fear that you would think I am giving up hope, abandoning my search for you. Perhaps I fear that myself. I wonder if others will question my motives. But I thought it would provide a distraction from the endless agony of waiting, some sense of normalcy. I was wrong.

Everyone greets me with pitiful eyes and awkward nods. I cannot escape. I asked to work with new clients, ones that don't know. It allows me a fresh challenge to keep my mind occupied. Another delusion I entertain.

4:15 am

I am not sure what you call it when you have a conversation with God—was it a dream or a nightmare? I remember as a child hearing about Moses and the burning bush, and it frightened me. Perhaps I am a little brash in my dealings with the Almighty, but I'm incensed that He knows where you are and won't help me find you. I asked Him if He knew you and how much you mean to me. He didn't reply. I glared at Him.

I hurled question after question, but He refused to answer. He didn't have form or shape, but I knew it was Him. I got the feeling He was nodding his head, like He understood. As my indignation vomited forth, I waited for His anger to consume me. I shouted and jeered, but sensed He's used to that and quite unfazed.

Then my rage turned to sobs, my knees folded and I pleaded, "Please, please, if you are real, I miss my son so much. Please let me see him."

I tried to make a deal, telling Him I would change if He gave me another chance to be with you. I lie before Him muttering, “Do you know my son? Do you know my son?”

Only then did He speak.

“I created him. Do *you* know *my* Son?”

Day 19

7:25 am

I hear hushed conversations echoing from the kitchen. You didn't know how to whisper, you know. I could hear everything—you telling Mom how many magic candles to put on my cake, giggling in anticipation of watching me try to blow them out. Rather, *you* unable to blow them out.

Because my birthdays were really more about you than me. Working so carefully to create a special drawing, coloring a home-made card, planning a surprise. Like everything, you gave it meaning.

I am 36 today, but feel like an old man gasping for his last breath. There will be no candles this year, no whispers from the kitchen, no birthday cards with funny-shaped hearts and big, awkward printed letters.

I wish I could lose myself in you. I now find constant focus on me oddly unsatisfying and empty.

10:30 am

Spivey didn't do it. He lied to police initially because he thought he would be a suspect. So he told them that he had been home all weekend, even tried to make things appear as if he had been. But cell phone records and credit card receipts have a way of making liars of everyone.

Turns out the convention he attended that weekend was less than savory. That and the websites he's been visiting. Now all the neighbors are aware of the animal amongst them. Would you ever sleep peacefully again?

I cannot tell you how relieved I am, yet we have lost our number one suspect. My only fear is that DeHart turns out to be an even more disgusting person.

3:35 pm

None of my birthday wishes are coming true, only my worst fears. I asked Donald Lufkin, the General Contractor in charge of the renovation, about Jimmy DeHart. Nothing but trouble, he said. The crew told Lufkin later that DeHart had bragged about being involved with underground characters that dealt in "drugs, laundering and children." I passed this along to Detective Graves. Great news on my birthday.

11:55 pm

I try to fool myself into believing that my heart is not wicked, that it is okay to indulge selfishness because my son is missing. But just because something tragic happened to me doesn't mean evil no longer dwells in my heart. It is tempting to allow sympathy to become my refuge, sorrow my excuse.

Am I becoming "the poor father who lost his son"? I fear I am becoming dependent upon this tragedy in order to create a new persona. Do I use this situation to manipulate others—after all, who would mistreat a grieving father? Do I use this heartache as an excuse for my own selfishness?

2:00 am

When you walked past me that Sunday morning, did I tell you I love you? Did I?

Because I do. So much, Robby. When was the last time you heard me say that? I hope it is not forgotten, I hope it is etched in your heart. I hope you hear it again and again wherever you are. I am so sorry I didn't tell you more often. So sorry.

Day 20

10:05 am

I don't know how to help your Mom. Talking only pierces the comfortable glaze and reveals pain. We used to plan our future months and years ahead. Now each minute is a life sentence. So we sit muted in our own worlds, our minds mired in cycles of anger, disbelief, guilt, fear and resolve. Sometimes they mix together and create a crude drink we've never tasted. Rarely do they produce hope.

I dwell in a prison with no escape. I retreat deep inside and isolate myself from the one person who could help. She thinks I am mad, she worries. But I am drowning in myself.

This tug-of-war with the fabric of my own character is tangible. I know she needs me and I push her away. I seek consolation in my own misery, but there is none.

I miss you. I miss the family we had.

6:45 pm

I dread coming home to this empty house. Empty of your constant chattering, toys concealing the hardwood, clothes hanging by a thread from the basement steps. Lifeless. Memories, only that now, just memories, the future packaged in a past I cannot retrieve.

So I took the long way home, driving past your school and the gym and the McDonald's where we'd stop just for the fries. I missed you sitting next to me in the truck, asking questions about whatever came to mind, fighting me for control of the dial. You never seemed impressed that Bob Edwards is to morning news what Walter Cronkite was to evening, never appreciated the subtle wit of Garrison Keillor. But I couldn't pry you from the truck on Saturday mornings when "Car Talk" came on. "Why do those guys talk so funny, Daddy?"

I can do whatever I want now, whenever I want, according to my schedule. I can walk in from work and take a nap. Eat when I am hungry. Read the paper in peace. Watch the news. Without competition.

But I miss the responsibility I kicked so hard against, that constant struggle between my pursuits and your needs. You gave me boundaries, a reason to look beyond myself.

I am left to myself without you. And that is frightening. I cannot hide anymore.

2:20 am

I found it. Buried underneath stacks of faded papers. A torn, yellowed clipping.

Tommy Stevens. He never saw his fifth birthday. The little body I saw covered with a sheet.

The jury said I wasn't to blame. At least not legally. *Not guilty of vehicular manslaughter.* I blamed the bottle, blamed circumstance, blamed the other driver. After all, he cut in front of me and I tried to stop. Perhaps I could have stopped quicker or veered away. Nonetheless, the courts said I was free.

But am I?

I wonder if Tommy's father has been. I remember hatred in his eyes.

Day 21

3:05 pm

I am holding your Martin Brodeur card in my hand. It is creased and crumpled, and I imagine the sweat from your hands made the cardboard softer. I trace my fingers to feel yours. A connection to you.

A man in Richmond called this morning and said he found your card in his restaurant. Even though it was badly worn, he figured it was important to some kid since the phone number was written on the back. He told me he'd place it in the mail if we still wanted it. I thanked him a thousand times and asked if I could pick it up today.

I know I have to call McAllister and Graves. But they will take the card and I want to hold onto it for a while. Savor it. Savor the fact that you had been touching this.

You left it on purpose so I would find you. And when I do, I will put this card back in your pocket.

4:30 pm

Tires squealed and thunder approached, followed by a futile effort to brake on gravel. I think a squad car dinged Graves' fender. The cloud of white dust stretched the length of the drive and soared above the pines.

I have never seen the FBI and police so energized. Seems like an entire battalion showed up at the house. I opened the door to breathless men hunting the only solid piece of evidence they had to date. They took the card from me, I knew they would, and dropped it into a transparent evidence bag.

As soon as I had recounted the details, about a dozen officers and agents yelled at once into radios and cell phones before hurrying off.

Graves lectured me for not calling immediately and for touching the evidence. I searched his eyes and he understood.

6:10 pm

So this may actually mean whoever took you lives up north. Maybe those clues to the south, like the van, were decoys.

At the Detective's urging, I spoke again to the media, knowing the captor is likely watching news reports. I told reporters that all clues still lead to a man traveling south.

We're coming to find you, son.

9:20 pm

I walked hesitantly tonight into that igloo we have called home the past three years. Coach Kania and Coach Fagan invited me to the tournament, and the Zamboni welcomed me, plodding in reassuring circles.

The parents are so awkward. They treat me as fragile glass. But the boys understand. They asked me to lace up skates, pull sweaters over pads, just like I would had you been there. I was tightening Chandler's laces when I noticed it.

The kids had hung your jersey in your locker. But you were not there to fill it out.

And I missed you then like never before.

I caught Cameron's eyes. He had removed the Captain's "C" from his sweater and sown it on yours.

I miss that locker room—the banter, little boys turned into giants among scattered piles of equipment, even the foul, damp smell. It means kids are playing hard, sweating, alive.

I stood broken at the end of the bench as the early evening sun poured through the windows and lit sections of the ice. There was something romantic about it, something pure and sentimental taking me to the days I skated outside as a young boy. Something about the way a melancholy sun says goodbye for the day, sharing its final light with the cold, hard surface you crave. It reminded me of the day you first gripped my hand on the ice, a day you needed me just to stand.

The sun caught fine sprays of ice, at once bursting into the air and suspended, lit up like magic dust in a Disney movie. Red and white stripes waved above the ice as The *Star Spangled Banner* echoed through the rink. I thought of you standing outside saluting the flag. I thought of the days when I heard you and Joey singing *The National Anthem* before you played basement hockey. But today no one cheered as the last chorus played.

The entire building hushed as players from both teams tapped their sticks against the ice, the reverent honor shown to an injured player. They continued above the official's whistles.

And then the kids did something even more beautiful. After a silent huddle, your teammates took the ice with only four players and a goalie. The officials motioned to the bench for a fifth skater. Before Coach Kania could open the door, Alexander skated over. You know, the quiet kid who keeps to himself.

"Coach, we're playing with four and that's all there is to it."

He skated back to take the face off and they played their hearts out. Four players against the opponent's five. Only one defenseman, always short one man.

I watched most of that game with glassy eyes and parched lips. It was the most magnificent game I have ever seen.

We lost 6-1.

Day 22

11:30 am

So if the Preacher is right, then I suppose this God of his understands what I am going through. The thing is, God supposedly gave His own son to be killed. Why would you do that to your own son? And why would Jesus willingly submit to that fate? I know in Greek and Roman mythology the gods interacted with humans and did bizarre things to avenge grievances, but I never remember any god giving his own life for inferiors. Never remember Mohammed or Buddha giving their lives like that. Was it really necessary to have all that carnage on the cross? Really. I guess it never seemed real to me, but now I understand how horrific it would be to lose your son. But why?

I am trying to sort this out in my head, but everything is a jumbled mess. It is too quiet. No one knocks on the door anymore except policemen. No kids laughing and screaming, no television and radio blaring together, no toys and clothes strewn carelessly, no parties and playdates with pizza and ice cream. Just boring adult stuff. And this dreadful silence.

I feel like a hypocrite. I used to mock prisoners who suddenly "found God." Used to dismiss it as a crutch for failures or people who couldn't rely on themselves. And yet I find myself in the same position. I don't want to turn blindly to God because it will make me feel better and give me hope, if that hope is based simply in *my* belief. I want to have some assurance that the God to whom I trust my eternal destiny has the power to grant it.

I know that I want to be with you. And right now I'm not doing too well on my own. For the first time, I *can't* do it alone.

I don't trust fables and fairy tales, though your unwavering faith in Santa Claus made me believe again. But I cannot attribute the majestic sunsets over Carmel, the purity of a

New England snow or the simple beauty of the trees and sky to the work of random chance. The fragile balance of life begs for the divine.

I am not sure I want to come face to face with it right now. I am ashamed of the man I see in your reflection. I suppose that's what the cross is for that the preacher talks about.

I keep asking Him where you are. Like I am going to cut a deal with the Almighty, some swap in which He returns my son in exchange for believing in His Son. Still, I get the sense that He doesn't cut deals. Apparently he laid his hand on the table, or the cross so to speak, two thousand years ago.

Do you know my son?

6:05 pm

School starts tomorrow, Robby. Your teachers and friends are going to miss you. You were all boy, full of testosterone and energy, but with a good sense of right and wrong. You stood up for the little kids, befriended the outcasts. I am the one they don't want back in that school. Always inciting the kids, getting in trouble for juggling chicken fingers at lunch to prompt giggles, or perhaps make milk come out a kid's nose. I want to do that again this year, okay?

It's difficult for Mom to see the back-to-school supplies lining the shelves at Target. I can't seem to break through to her. I whisper "I love you", but she doesn't blush and look up with the sparkle in her eyes anymore. It's like the love we shared was made complete when you were born. You gave definition to our lives, made us look outside ourselves. And in doing so, we found purpose.

Your mom stares out the window, and her sadness runs down the panes like drops of rain.

10:45 pm

I am tormented by guilt, Robby. You are out there and what am I doing? The same as ever. Thinking about me, wondering how this affects me. One minute I felt like the greatest father in the world. But then something small would happen. You got sick, came down with a cold.

And what were my first thoughts? What an inconvenience it was. I hate to admit that. Your sickness ruined my plans for the night, the work I had planned, our dinner out.

Why do I seem so willing to help others when they have needs, but not those closest to me? Is it so they will recognize my goodness? Am I trying to earn favor with God through the good words of strangers who don't know the nature of my heart? I am learning that the true measure of a man is how he treats those closest to him, those who cannot be deceived by pretense.

12:10 am

No updates from the police today. Either they are stuck or they are silent for a reason.

3:20 am

I woke up in a cold sweat. Another nightmare. I see your face filled with terror, your arms outstretched toward me, but you keep slipping further away. I feel anguish choking you, see the horror that has become your eyes.

My heart thumped so hard it woke your Mom. I grabbed a dry shirt, slipped from the bedroom and passed your room, bathing in the soft glow of your nightlight we still leave on.

I peeked inside, as I have every night for eight years, hoping to catch a glimpse of you sprawled out and twisted in covers, head swathed in your hooded sweatshirt, one leg dangling over the edge, mouth open and little hands gripping your favorite toy.

But you were not there. I stared, hoping to make you appear, but you don't.

So, I rock slowly on the front porch, gazing at low, airy clouds drifting in front of the moon. I never noticed before that black shadows drape the yard even in darkness.

I notice all the little things now.

Day 23

9:45 am

They nabbed DeHart in Miami. Apparently, he's not painting houses anymore. The only colors he mixes are green cash and white powder.

I don't need to know his sordid details, only if he has you.

7:20 pm

Your picture flashes on the screen all day and thrusts reality deeper into my bones. Sometimes your photo appears and it seems real. Then I realize it's only an image, the news remains grim, aching dispels hope.

Reporters repeat your physical characteristics, but they can't define your inner qualities. They see a cute little boy, but they don't *know* you.

They don't know the generous heart that wants to feed the homeless. They don't know the boy who gathers his toys to share with poor children. They don't hear you ask me about your favorite hockey players, "Daddy, does he help people? Does he donate money and spend time with sick kids?" Because that's your goal in life, to help people.

They don't know an eight-year-old boy who has an old man's understanding of the human heart. Not to mention an old man's penchant for watching *The Weather Channel*. At any given time, you know the weather patterns affecting every country on the planet. But more importantly, you can feel the emotion inside people. You see a video or hear a song, and you feel pain and loneliness, or joy and hope. You understand the human heart.

Whether I see your picture or not, my every thought is drawn to you, Robby. You are different, so very different. The world needs more of you. We need more of you.

9:20 pm

I won an award to be presented this fall in New York City. Best copy for a consumer print ad. I am not sure if they gave it to me out of pity or just reward. Yes, I am following in the proud path of that great paragon of intellect in the world of advertising, Derwood Stevens. An honored man, for sure.

Should I stand before them as the frail, pitiful father who lost his son, moving my peers to tears and a certain standing ovation by dedicating this award to my son, telling them that I am honored by their recognition, but that it means nothing compared to you?

Or should I tell them the cold, hard truth? That I won this award at the expense of my son. That when I should have been enjoying you, playing with cars, reading a book together, talking on the front porch, my mind was running with this ad concept? Should I tell them that I gained more satisfaction from creating a great tagline than from discovering something new and beautiful inside you?

The biggest challenge for a man is not achieving success in business. Who cannot? Hard work, focus, determination and a little bit of smarts. Heck, look at the dopey guys in suits who run these companies—you think they are all that bright or gifted? No, the biggest challenge for a man is not building his business or his career.

It is laying it down, no longer craving the adrenaline rush from a new project or overcoming a challenge. It is deciding not to take refuge in work, and instead finding that same satisfaction in a baby's first words, a toddler's first steps, an eight-year-old boy's simple wish to play basketball with his Dad, discovering something wonderful taking shape inside your little boy's heart and mind. It is relinquishing control of that which you can control and making yourself vulnerable to that which you cannot control, namely the most important people in your life. I can run a large company, could make it on my own through pure sweat and perseverance, but ask me to deal with a problem you are having at school and I cower and retreat, leaving it to Mom or chance.

I am sorry I missed the magic in every moment, sorry I did not lay it down for you before. I am an ad man, I get paid to spin words, but there is no spinning this, what I have become inside. You are teaching me how to be a man, I hope it is not too late.

11:35 pm

I miss mussed hair that never met a brush, clothes that didn't fit let alone match. I miss the way you would parade your independence one moment, then sit with your hand on my knee the next. I miss strolling the campus, feeling the warmth of your hand in mine. I like it that you held my hand and didn't care what others thought. Maybe you didn't know that eight-year-old boys don't hold their father's hands. And I think I like that even better.

2:10 am

The bottle is calling me again. To drown out this hell, but perhaps it caused this in the first place. Little Tommy Stevens. He would have been, what, twenty-four now? Maybe graduated from college, starting a new job, perhaps getting married to his sweetheart.

We have nothing. No leads, no hope.

Day 24

1:55 pm

DeHart may be guilty of a lot of things, but taking you is not one of them. His alibis checked out. Every one of them. Doesn't even remember my name. I was probably one in a long line of people who had trouble with him.

The child in the car was apparently his own. Another crime against humanity.

My relief is momentary. I toil in despair because all our leads are drying up. It isn't Spivey, it isn't DeHart. Who then? I have hope that you are alive. We have no evidence to the contrary.

4:30 pm

I think I found him. Thomas Stevens. Still lives outside of Baltimore. Could he have carried bitterness all these years? He swore he would get me for taking his son from him. But that was nineteen years ago, a lifetime. I lived in fear for the first year or so afterward, but then I went off to college, met your Mom and it was like it never happened.

I buried the memories deep inside, like so many of my faults, and made them disappear, like records collecting dust in a tattered cardboard box.

Not sure I can tell Graves and McAllister yet. Your Mom doesn't even know about the accident.

It can't be him, can it? Would he have tracked me down? Would his heart have stayed broken that long, the bitterness festering for two decades? I guess I know the answer to that. I understand the desperation.

But would he really take my son?

7:45 pm

A soft rain welcomes dusk as I consider the streets of gold the choir sang about last weekend. Their voices soared with visions of mansions waiting in the Holy City. And it disturbed me.

I try to reconcile the irony of people who profess that greed is evil, yet yearn for material riches in heaven. I am confused because my understanding is that the promise of heaven is enjoying relationships with loved ones and God for eternity.

They can have their streets of gold.

I'll take a gravel drive as long as it leads to you.

2:45 am

A day does not pass that I do not hear the voice of a child, glance out the window and hope to see a little boy caught up in his own little world bounding toward the house.

Yet morbid thoughts own me. It's been almost a month. Perhaps you were taken from me so I never had to witness the wonder of a little boy's heart ebbing toward cynicism, so that I could believe myself. Another of your subtle gifts to me. I would never tell Mom, but I pictured your funeral tonight—how you would want it done. Not the way everyone else would do it.

I see only children, no adults. Your teammates wear their jerseys and carry their sticks. Each recalls a poignant act, some quiet deed that showed them how to be a better person, a better team. Afterward, they line up along your casket with one space unfilled and tap their sticks. You appear in that moment and fill it with your presence. The only sounds above the tapping are the sniffles and cries of eleven brave boys.

Your heaven would have no streets, only a fresh sheet of ice and blades that never dull. You would be buried wearing your hockey jersey, the "C" sown proudly on the chest. And with your beloved Martin Brodeur card, tattered and crumpled, tucked gently into your hand.

That's the way you would want to spend eternity.

Day 25

5:30 am

The FBI has begun to piece together a loose trail based on interviews with people who remember seeing a young boy and man in the town where you left your hockey card. They have not told me everything yet, possibly because they don't want to get our hopes up or have information leak to the media. But, Detective Graves told me the trail extends north to Baltimore and possibly into Pennsylvania.

I am going to see you soon. I am going to hold you and never let you go. I am going to kiss your little face and appreciate every tiny thing about you. I will be so different for you, Robby.

1:35 pm

Do you know how much people love you, Robby? The children in Anniston, Alabama made a giant card and had hundreds of people sign it for you. I put it in your room.

Remember the time we were driving to Destin, Florida? You never knew the name, just that it was the place with the white sand beaches, dolphins and go-karts. Waves of heat lifted off the highway when the truck broke down outside Anniston. And I thought our vacation would be ruined.

But along came a guy who pulled over to help us. Turned out he was the Mayor of Anniston. I told him our story and without flinching he made some calls to City Hall. Before we knew it, a tow truck had taken us into town and Mayor Chip drove us to a hotel whose owners put us up for free.

Two of his assistants, Shirley and Angie, took us to the Community Pool for an afternoon of fun. We spent a memorable weekend in that sleepy southern town, made some lifelong friends and even created the town slogan: *Welcome to Anniston, The Home of Southern Hospitality.*

You have an entire town thinking about you even now.

3:55 pm

I called Thomas Stevens' house. The man whose son I killed. A woman answered and said he would be back in a couple days. Could he have taken you? Could the bitterness and anger have lasted this long?

10:35 pm

Fireflies light the yard like multi-colored plastic lights strung at summertime parties. They are everywhere, and I imagine they miss you chasing them. I imagine they miss the warmth of your skin and the curious look in your eyes before you softly blow them to freedom.

I wonder why children are our cruelest mirror, exposing our shortcomings against their simplicity. How many times did I curse under my breath when you allowed a scorer past, not because you let your team down, but because I thought you let me down? Why did I look away and make excuses for your imperfection? Why didn't I encourage you? I will do it right next time, Robby. I promise.

3:45 am

I woke up in a cold sweat. My hands refuse to stop shaking. The accident happened late in the summer. About the time you were taken. Was Thomas Stevens at his son's grave remembering that night like it was yesterday, feeling a pain that refused to be eased by the years, angry that the promise of a young boy had been stolen from him?

He *could have* done it.

Day 26

8:30 am

I asked Officer Bill if he would go visit Thomas Stevens with me while he is off duty. He can question neighbors and search for clues with a flash of his badge.

I cannot tell Graves and McAllister yet. I don't want word leaking to the media, don't want your Mom to have to deal with this, too. Secrets are an evil unto themselves.

The file is sealed because I was seventeen and a minor, so no one can access my record. I know Bill could lose his job for helping me. Still, he said he'd think about it, but strongly advised me to tell the police.

12:45 pm

The August sun is a hammer against dry nails, the air syrupy and adamant. But I feel so cold inside.

I am an empty shell of a man, Robby. I used you and all the distractions of life to hide my emptiness. I covered it up. But now I am stripped bare and hold nothing of my own.

I am thirty-six and I want to be like you. To wake up with a quiet confidence and self-assurance. You are that way already. That's what I meant when I used to look at you and say, "You're so cool, Robby." I like it that when grown-ups disparage your New York Yankees, you don't back down. I like it that when other kids wear their clothes one way and you the opposite, you are completely comfortable. Even accomplished men don't have that ease about themselves. Perhaps you know where your identity comes from, therefore no one can give it and no one can take it away. How did I become so oblivious to truth while you embrace it?

I wish I had not wasted time trying to change you, but instead enjoyed you. I fought for so long to make you into someone else's image. The sports star, the perfect student, well-mannered with social graces. You are none of those things.

You are who you are, no pretenses, no apologies. You know I love you, but do you know I *like* you as much?

3:15 pm

I have to go inside. The bus comes soon. Brakes squeal, children squeal. Scruffy runs to see you, but you are not there. She comes galloping up the gravel drive, alone.

Another reminder that you aren't getting off the bus, you aren't coming home.

10:45 pm

The police are completely thrown by clues leading to both the south and the north. Seems the leads they were piecing together have hit a dead end. Whoever took you had planned an elaborate scheme to distract them.

Tomorrow morning we drive to Baltimore to find Thomas Stevens. Am I going there to find you or to seek closure on an unfinished chapter in my life? Will he revel in my sorrow, thinking it justice for my mistake?

I have always told myself it was an accident, it wasn't intentional. And that's true. If he did this, it is unforgivable.

12:22 am

It's been twenty-six days. You are gone. And I am lost. Everything seemed so normal that morning. And now nothing is the same.

I am sitting on the front porch. You and I are awake and this is our time. I was given eight short years with you, not nearly enough to carry me to old age. I have memories, each one now so vivid and infinitely more precious than anything else. But that is all I have, all they are. The past.

Pitter-patters that had turned to thuds woke me to pale strands of sun softly lighting the room. You came barging through the door, your pant legs rubbing against each other, then tiptoed as you neared the bed, not understanding you had woken us when you opened the door.

"Daddy," you whispered, "will you come downstairs with me?"

"Sure, give me a few minutes with Mom, okay?"

Two minutes later, you repeated the scene.

"Daddy, why have you been so long? It's been thirty minutes!"

You scampered away once satisfied I was rolling out of bed. You didn't understand weekends were made for sleeping. I swear you must have been a rooster in a previous life. I came downstairs at 6:22 and found you there, apparently trying your hand at three different activities simultaneously.

"Hi, Daddy!" you chirped.

Crayons and markers wrestled on the floor with sweatpants and shirt strewn at your whim. The remaining markers slowly rolled off the edge of the coffee table, propelled forward by your incessant pounding. Across the arms of a chair, an inside-out sleeve dangled from its precipice slightly above the floor. The box for the video propped at an angle against the wall, hanging wide open.

The world you turned upside down every day by your presence seems hopelessly spinning out of control with your disappearance.

Day 27

9:30 pm

I found him. Stood face-to-face with the nightmare that quietly haunted me for years.

I shook as I approached a front yard besieged with yellow and orange plastic toys. A little picnic table and slide, a three-wheeler.

He was outside watering plants. I introduced myself, said my name slowly and let it sink in. I braced myself for anger, for fury, for gloating and hatred.

I did not expect compassion.

He told me his story. The bitterness consumed him and his first marriage. He sought help, let it go and began a new life. As he told me the story, his face shone like some of the people in church. Could have been the reflection of the evening sun, I don't know. All I kept thinking was this is a free man, and I am the one imprisoned. And then he took out the key and unlocked the door.

"I forgive you. You didn't know what you were doing, you were only a kid. We'll pray that you find your son."

He should have been glad at my loss. Instead he was distraught.

He called his little boy over to say hello. And I saw *you*. My lips trembled and I reached for him. I touched his hands, clammy and dirty. And warm. His warm skin.

I couldn't stay. I apologized for bothering him, apologized for the past.

Where do I go from here? A piece of my past has been made whole, but everything is in the past. That night when I was seventeen. The last time I saw you twenty-seven days ago. Memories of you. All in the past. How does any of this change the future?

10:35 pm

I went for a ride tonight. I missed you next to me in the truck and longed for our next father-son trip. Just the two of us. No distractions, no phone calls, no emails. You and me, from sunrise to midnight every day. I try to coax you each year to pursue the warm beaches of Florida during spring training. Watch baseball on grassy hillsides all morning and relax in the sand all afternoon. How did you ever persuade me to agree to New Jersey? In March. To see your favorite hockey team in a frozen arena.

We drove for hours, talking, recording the outside temperature every five minutes, keeping track of license plates. I remember tucking you in at the end of the first day in New York City. You looked up and mumbled, "Daddy, I didn't know you could fit so much into one day." We skated at Rockefeller Center, scaled the Empire State Building at twilight, negotiated the subway and studied people for hours. We returned to the hotel, strolled to a corner grocery store, picked up a quart of milk and cereal, then sat on the edge of the bed enjoying our midnight snack and ESPN highlights.

We exulted in those first steps into NHL arenas, the energy and driving music drawing us in. We soaked up every spray of the ice, every goal greeted with thunderous applause. We were the first ones in, the last ones out. We played hockey in the corridors and people loved watching you sprawled across dirty, concrete floors making incredible saves while I kicked a rubber puck at you.

They were the most wonderful days of my life. Just you and me, all day and all night. Like a Mastercard commercial. Priceless. Only better.

How I want to plan our trip for next year. New Jersey never sounded so lovely.

1:30 am

I walk into your room to catch a peek of you before going to bed, and you are not there.

A night never passed that I did not walk into your room and stare at you. The innocence and purity of exactly who you were. When you were sleeping, there were no insecurities, no hurts, no anxiety. No matter if we had had a fight or a special day together, the feelings were always the same.

He is my son. He is my legacy.

I want another chance to kiss you goodnight. Another chance to read you a bedtime story, to hear you say, "I love you, Daddy." Another chance to tell you how much I love you.

We have no leads. Only sorrow.

There are no second chances, only eternal choices made on carefree summer mornings.

Day 28

10:30 am

I never knew real love until I felt the pant of your breath on my chin, your tiny fingers clinging to me, your head nestled into my chest.

I love your Mom, but it cannot compare. We made vows to support and love each other, but always remain aware that we receive something in return.

But a child is given to us helpless and dependent. There is nothing he can give back, no way to express gratitude for love given unselfishly. Perhaps this is what makes parenting fulfilling and why marriages become stagnant. Two people stop sacrificing, stop seeking the other's happiness above their own.

There are no vows exchanged with a baby, only a promise from parent to child. No guarantees. The child could grow up to resent or love his parents. Yet parents sacrifice and give with the knowledge that they are training their child to eventually leave.

And find someone they will ultimately love more than their parents.

I can never love anyone more than you, Robby.

4:35 pm

I looked forward to the game all week. A pleasant diversion if there can be such a thing. I feel close to you there. I arrived early to watch other teams play. Parents grumbled about Coach Kania letting the team play with only four skaters—"doesn't he know we'll lose," they muttered. But the kids voted 11-0 to play shorthanded until you come back to fill the fifth spot.

A handful of parents tried to persuade Coach into playing five. The *parents* don't want to lose. The *kids* understand they already have if they don't play with four.

Every player wore your number tonight, a little “30” sewn onto every sleeve. You should have seen them skate, Robby. They played through weary legs and scrapped for every loose puck. Joey was an acrobat in net, shutting the other team down.

The score was tied with four minutes left. The kids were digging in the corners, hitting the ice to block shots, diving to keep the puck in the zone, jamming for every opportunity. Just one more goal. With two minutes left, Coach pulled Joey for an extra skater. The first time all night we had an even number of skaters.

Cameron broke free and took a crisp pass from Chandler at center ice and glided over the blue line, but a defenseman got back just in time. Cam’s legs were rubber, but he managed to fire a wrist shot that sailed through the air in slow motion. Clunk, right off the cross bar and along the goal line. Keith scrambled for the loose puck and shoveled it to Alexander, who put it home for the winning goal. You should have seen them celebrate, Robby.

After the game, the kids asked me to celebrate with them, knowing I needed to smile. And so for a few minutes I let myself go and reveled in your friends and their victory.

But after awhile it grew quiet. The kids knew there was a time to celebrate, and a time to reflect. Each one retreated into himself to summon the strength to win the next game.

Before I left, Alexander approached me with the game puck. The puck he had earned.

"This is for Robby. Will you put this in his room so he can have it when he comes home?"

You know I'm not sure about the whole thing with God, but I believe I have seen Him in that locker room. And if He's anything like those kids, then I am a believer.

9:20 pm

An odd term finds itself swathed around my heart tonight, one that fathers don't ordinarily use to describe their sons. Respect. I respect you, Robby, the sum of who you are even at a young age.

You have been created this way for a reason, to do some great and noble good for people. I like that you are different. It gives you depth and a unique texture. You stand amidst 18,000 Toronto Maple Leafs fans and wear your New Jersey sweater defiantly, challenging anyone who dares dismiss your team—even if they are three times your size. You turn your heart toward the homeless and ask to work at the soup kitchen when playtime outside beckons. That's why people respect you.

You have so much to give, so much promise. You are my legacy. What else is there to accomplish on this earth? Do I want to be remembered for ads that helped sell more software? Or do I want to be remembered for what I gave to my son?

I should have told you all these things long ago. Please, please give me another chance.

12:15 am

None of this means anything unless we find you, Robby. Graves and McAllister believe you were taken north through Maryland into Pennsylvania. Ditching the van in South Carolina was a ruse to send us in the wrong direction. They have clues, I know they do, but they are leaving me in the dark, perhaps to keep the media there as well.

The animal who took you planned this out thoroughly, which makes it all the more heinous. I try to crowd the horrifying images out of my head, but nothing works.

You used to miss me after being away for a night. Sometimes when you brought a friend along on vacation, you would hug me goodnight and tell me you missed me. Even though we had been together all day. You missed our time alone. I know the pain a father feels without his son; I cannot imagine your fear and loneliness.

I will find you, Robby. And I will get whoever has done this to you. I will make him pay.

Day 29

11:30 am

This Preacher has an interesting way of communicating ideas out of that dusty old Book. Like when he gave me the definition of heaven and hell. He said today that God has adopted us. Never thought about God in these terms before. I thought religion involved obeying a list of rules, you know, some checklist like the *7 Habits* that you master to earn your way through the pearly gates. All religions seem to have a similar list, but to be different, they put their own twists on them, I guess. But *this* is different. He's not talking about *religion*, he's talking about a *relationship*, between a father and a son. I get that.

I feel this uncomfortable prodding inside. When he spoke about God adopting us as His sons, it hit home. I told you that's why I think it is so cool that you are adopted. For some couples, having a baby is a surprise, a chance happening. But we picked you especially. Your Mom and I couldn't have children. Robby, even before you were born, we wanted you. You are all we ever wanted.

When we first heard about your birth mother being pregnant,

Robby, I hadn't considered this…

2:45 pm

Graves and McAllister grilled me for two hours, asking why I hadn't mentioned that you were adopted. It never crossed my mind. We have always considered you our flesh and blood. You've always been our little Robby, we never made a distinction.

The birth father wasn't interested. In fact, he had threatened the birth mom and coerced her into ending the pregnancy. Until she saw pictures of a tiny fetus with toes and fingers forming, a baby's eyes and ears taking shape, a child's heart beating. She knew that was you, and that you were special.

It couldn't be him. Why would he want you *now*?

You were our promise, all we ever wanted. A little boy in whose eyes we swam, with a smile that chased away clouds. I need to gaze into those same eyes and feel the warmth of your smile again, feel your little hand curled up in mine. We saved you once. We will save you again, Robby.

5:20 pm

The FBI began hunting for Scott Downing before they left the house. I have no idea where he lives. It's been so long and he wasn't around at your birth. There can be no good reason why he would kidnap a bright, happy little boy and terrify him. I wish I could get to him first.

Your birth mother loved you, Robby. But she couldn't take care of you properly, and we wanted you.

There is hope, Robby. There is hope. I may yet tuck you into bed and hear your giggle again.

Day 30

9:15 am

The FBI is enlisting help from the public, plastering Downing's face on the television screen next to yours. I shudder.

Who is this foul man that he should plunder your simple dreams and destroy your innocence? I don't care about his sad childhood. He is responsible for his actions. I don't want to hear anyone make excuses for him. Excuses will not restore your innocence. Nor will they save him.

1:00 pm

The FBI reassured me that this is the most favorable scenario. They wouldn't make any promises, but seemed genuinely relieved that it may be the biological father.

The criminal psychologists think he may have taken you to make some kind of connection with the birth mother.

All I know is that there are hundreds of law enforcement officers swarming in different cities where Scott Downing grew up and lived most recently. They are hungry to find a missing child alive.

3:30 pm

I am going to see you soon, I know it. And I am going to tell you all the things I like about you. I know you can hear me even now. So I will tell you, Robby.

I like it that you ask whether sports stars visit sick children, not how much money they make. I like it that you amble carefree down the driveway with lemonade and Goldfish in hand for your best friend while you won't walk two feet to pick up a stick for me. I like it that you ask me to hold you after I discipline you. I like the way you make your teeth loose and pull them so that the tooth fairy brings you money. I like it that you still believe the tooth fairy is a girl with tiny little wings. I like the way you make sandwiches leaving more peanut butter and jelly on the counter than on the bread. I like the way you grab my rental car keys before a trip, put them softly to your nose and say, "It smells like a rental car." And then tuck the keys under your pillow and sleep on them so I can't leave without seeing you.

I like you telling me not to tickle you, knowing that's exactly what you want. I like playing grumpy bear in bed in the morning. I like matted hair when you wake up. I like your hand resting on my knee. I like lying in bed talking, faces turned to each other only inches away. I like seeing your eyes lit up, fighting weariness so you can stay up and talk longer. I like that you name your hockey sticks and make me say goodnight to them. I like falling asleep scratching your back. I like my little boy.

Day 31

11:45 am

Downing was seen with a small boy in a remote northeastern Pennsylvania town six days ago. I cannot believe you are missing. And I cannot believe you are still alive, the odds say otherwise. It's like I am trapped in a dream, but experiencing every emotion.

A child identified you from the picture on television. The owner of a small market recalls selling Downing groceries, including Lucky Charms. Your favorite. Could be coincidence, could be you.

4:30 pm

We have been glued to the television today, hanging on every lead, every word of another sighting, cheering on the media for once. Just hope it doesn't panic Downing so that he does something irrational.

7:45 pm

Through the heaviness, I think I spotted a smile on your Mom's face today. Okay, maybe it wasn't a smile, but a slight upturn to relieve the despair.

I hope that in a few days when I walk into your bathroom I see your towel perched in its favorite position, sprawled across the floor. I hope I see red and white and green toothpaste smeared across the vanity, the tube a mangled mess as if you had been wrestling an alligator. I hope I find pools of water everywhere but in the sink.

Then I will know my son is home.

11:30 pm

He shattered your innocence and tried to steal your future. Will you trust anyone again or play outside with carefree joy? Or will you live your life looking over your shoulder?

I hope he is looking over his. Because I am coming after him. I hold revenge in my hands even now.

3:30 am

I had a dream that I did it.

It was a cold, drizzly morning. I walked briskly through downtown with death in my pocket. I couldn't feel anything except the weight, my sagging coat a constant reminder that I carried justice with me, the power to take life. I hopped the long marble steps up the judicial building, breathed a heavy sigh and continued flint-eyed, seeking Downing.

He sat in the courtroom in plain brown clothes, smug and unconcerned with the horror he had caused, a man without a conscience. I hurried toward him.

I reached my trembling hand inside my coat pocket and felt the cold, hard steel.

My palms were sweaty and slipping across the handle, my finger slowly drawing the trigger, my heart racing through my chest. I thought the whole courtroom could hear it pounding, could feel the hatred fill that small room. He stood and turned to me and I looked into cold, hollow eyes. The same eyes I had pictured in the mirror so many times. An empty, soulless man.

And I did it.

I cannot believe it even now. I have never felt that sensation, the rush of adrenaline mixing with euphoria and fear and dread. I was lost in the moment, like I was watching it from afar. And in an instant, two lives changed direction for eternity.

I didn't mean to do it. It just happened.

My finger slowly released from the trigger. I backed up and time stopped. And then my mouth opened and I swear I didn't move my lips, but out came the three most powerful words I have ever spoken.

I forgive you.

I don't know why those words came out. Perhaps because I had felt their power myself.

And for the first time, I felt free. I have lived my entire life as my own god. But in that moment I reflected the true image of God.

I fear that you would think it a betrayal that I forgave the man who took you. Even writing such a thing is repugnant to me, but for once I feel that in doing so I would have done the right thing. And I think you would agree.

One day, I will still testify before a judge that Downing doesn't deserve to see daylight again. He will have to face his own guilt for taking an innocent child. But I will not be his judge.

I cannot bear the life sentence of my own bitterness.

Day 32

6:30 am

I just heard your voice for the first time in over a month! I am sorry I could barely utter a word, Robby. All I could do was weep and tell you that I love you. You are coming home! In a few hours, you will be here.

The house will be messy and loud again. Clothes and toys and markers and food will be scattered about. Friends will giggle, dogs will bark and birds will sing once again.

Graves, McAllister and dozens of FBI Agents swarmed on Downing as he slept early this morning. What kind of person can sleep when he has taken an innocent boy from his parents? The psychologists were right. Downing had apparently reconnected with your birth mother, but she didn't want a relationship with him. His twisted logic convinced him that bringing you there would help them reconcile. I don't care anymore about him, his sick thinking or pathetic life. All I know is that you are coming home, Robby.

One month from today we will celebrate your birthday. Nine years ago you changed my life.

I can hear your voice so sweet and innocent, always with the same pitch asking about that day. And I imagine it will remain the same even when you turn sixteen. "Daddy, tell me about the day I was born."

And I recount the story as I have countless times. Crisp autumn breezes cradled leaves in their wings and the sun reigned over a cloudless day. Your birth mother called us at 10:26 that morning to let us know it was time. The expectation left us speechless, wearing smiles in the waiting room.

Four hours later, at 2:19, a nurse quite taken with her bundle strolled toward us. We didn't know if you were going to be a girl or boy, but we had names picked out. Kelley for a girl,

Robby for a boy. Your Mom and I peeked down and saw the most gorgeous baby with brown hair. And I screamed, "It's a Robby! It's a Robby!"

And when I see you coming toward me in a few hours, I will be yelling, "It's my Robby! It's my Robby!"

A New Day

2:20 am

You are upstairs sleeping, Martin Brodeur card in one hand, puck resting under the other. You sleep soundly, as if nothing happened. I cannot close my eyes.

The nightmare is over. When I saw the flashing lights approaching this afternoon, I thought my heart would burst. I sprinted to the police car so fast the officer had to skid sideways to avoid running into me. I saw your sandy brown hair in the backseat, saw you alive, and I couldn't wait to hold you.

How do I explain how I feel? I cannot. Joy, relief, gratitude. I have been given a second chance. All I could do is weep and sob and hold you, hold all three of us. I saw tears flow from hardened officers as we walked toward our car. I could not take my eyes off you, did not want to let you out of my sight. I couldn't let go of your warm hands against mine. I am sorry if it was awkward driving home. I know I didn't say much and Mom couldn't stop crying, but my heart was gasping for air and words could not escape through my smile.

Robby, you are beautiful. You are warm and alive, I cannot stop saying that. You are a gift and I will never forget that. Have I told you today I love you? Have I told you a thousand times? Because that is not enough. I will show you this time.

Through your childlikeness, you taught me how to be a man. Through your innocent devotion, you taught me how to be a son. Though I lost you for a month here, I gained eternity with you. Because when I thought I had lost my son, I found His Son.

I am glad there are second chances after all. Today, I was granted a second chance. Today, a father and his son reunited.

I will feel your warm hand folded into mine forever.

I think I will go sit by your bed and watch you until you wake.

Epilogue

As far as I know, my husband never wrote another word, at least not in that journal.

Two years ago, my son graduated from high school. The celebration was short-lived. That summer he was diagnosed with leukemia. My husband never recovered from the news. He would lie in bed at night and sob, afraid of losing the boy he had grown to love beyond anything in this world. He knew eternity held the promise of reunion, but if one month apart had been unbearable, how could he survive years without his son?

He died eighteen months later from a sudden heart attack. There were no blocked arteries or history of heart problems.

My husband had given this journal to my son, to sustain him in his fight. And before leukemia took Robby, he wrote the final entry that follows. As much for me, I think—

something for me to hold onto, to comfort me when I would be alone—as it was for him to feel close to his father.

I wonder about my boys, what they are doing right now.

So I return to gaze through these windows. Content to look beyond the high lofty clouds sweeping in before the storm, able to finally see the subtle intricacies of life that play before me. I can see through those clouds and into heaven itself. And there I know my two boys will remain as shadows holding hands. If there are mansions there and streets of gold and myriad people and angels, they will never notice.

They will find a quiet spot alone, sitting with legs swinging above a bridge, skipping stones across a placid stream, talking and laughing, wishing the day would never end, and finally having their wish come true.

A Letter of Homecoming

Dear Dad,

Do you know the thoughts that meander like a gentle stream through a son's mind when he lies alone late at night, apart from his father, feeling death creep into his hospital room?

He thinks about the endless hours his father spent with him, about the days and nights when he needed a soft shoulder or a firm hand. He thinks about the man unafraid to share his frailties and become vulnerable to his fears, the man who was not yet a man but became one, a man who had the courage to change and give his son the best gift he could ever have: a father.

Dad, when that man took me those many summers ago, do you know what sustained me? The fact that you had never broken a promise to me. I kept hearing your voice say, "I will find you."

"Do you promise?" I would ask.

And I heard your reply. “I promise.”

That’s all I needed.

A little boy knows only innocence, no black, no gray, just white. All I knew is that you were always there. At my games, at my school, in the basement playing hockey. Your mind may have been elsewhere, but you were there when you could have been somewhere else. A little boy doesn’t know good and bad fathers, just whether he has one or not. And mine was always there.

You didn’t want a perfect little boy. I didn’t want a perfect father.

The fact is that you were there, you did what was right. And after you found me, you changed. You didn’t make empty promises.

You started your own business so you could work from home and never miss a moment with me. You taught me your business so that we could do it together and because, I later found out, you knew I would have a difficult time working for someone else.

I wonder who I got that from?

You took me with you everywhere, to meetings with your attorney and accountant and consultants. You let me make mistakes that cost you money and still you remained patient.

I will never forget the countless days we sat next to each other at Liz's Cafe on that lazy leather sofa. You would buy me a blueberry muffin and milk, and we'd sit there for hours, each of us working silently.

I was too young to express the peace and joy I felt there with you. Just the two of us, enjoying nothing more than being together. You would help me with my schoolwork, and you'd let me help you, you made me feel important.

That's what I think about lying here with eyes heavy, heart

soft and fading.

And I know you started your own business so you could be with me when I came home from school. I can only imagine how anxious you felt every afternoon when the bus stopped, wondering if I would get off. When you heard the crunching of the gravel and saw me coming, you stood up on the front porch and put your work down, and I could see relief on your face. And your smile welcomed me home.

I looked forward to that smile all day.

And once your work was down, it stayed down. You met me at the top of the drive and as I slung my backpack off, you took it from me and threw your arms around me.

Nothing ever felt better, Dad. We sat on the steps of the porch and ate popsicles together, talked about my day at school. You listened and your mind wasn't elsewhere.

You knew me. Every struggle, every triumph, every laugh, every tear. My first broken heart.

When I told you that Emmi Caldwell broke up with me, I saw tears escape your eyes though I fought mine. It was only puppy love, I know that now and you surely knew then, but I was hurting and you hurt with me.

Do you know how hard you were on yourself, Dad?

We had our fights, some bad ones, perhaps because we were so much alike. But at the end of the day, we forgave each other and you'd put your head against mine and look straight into my eyes. Do you know how many times throughout the years I would be in a difficult situation and close my eyes, just so I could see yours, eyes that believed in me without measure?

They are the same eyes I look to for strength now. The same arms that make me feel safe, that ease my burdens. When the pain is too much to bear, memories become my comfort and eternity my hope.

I can still see that look of joy on your face when you would whisper to me, “No matter what happens, son, I’m going to be there with you. I’m going to be there.”

Seems like the sun always came out when you told me that.

When I lie awake at night, my body losing the fight, that is what I think of. I think of your arms around me, wishing I were nine again, wishing you could be here to hold me. When I slip out of this world into the next, this is the thought I will carry with me.

You meeting me on the gravel drive, slipping the weight off my back, replacing it with the warmth and strength of your arms, welcoming me home.

This disease is taking me. I know it will not be long, Dad. I only have one request if you can hear me now.

When you hear the crunching of the gravel, promise you will run to meet me.

In Memoriam

Brandon M. Coker
1985 - 2002

Though his time with us was as the passing of a shadow, he brought many lifetimes of joy and love to family and friends.

May he live through eternity as he did on earth,
full of God's grace and peace.

Well done, my good and faithful servant.

SHADE OF THE MAPLE
BY KIRK MARTIN

Anna Matthews left home at eighteen, a young woman rooted in small-town virtues, seeking adventure in the Green Mountains of Vermont. She found a free-spirited young man whose boundless imagination captivated her heart. Forced apart, Anna tries to build a new life.

A decade later, a series of gripping novels awaken Anna's veiled dreams, illuminating a striking disparity within her marriage. She seeks the author, but the truth she discovers will change her life. Anna is confronted with a clear choice—continue living the comfortable, but hollow American Dream or pursue *her* dream.

Experience a love story as large and timeless as the Vermont landscape. Share the quest of two restless people finding peace and consuming intimacy in each other. See your dreams reflected in this triumph of enduring love.

Kirk is donating $1.00 from every purchase to breast cancer research.

SHADE OF THE MAPLE
WHAT READERS ARE SAYING

Kirk Martin's lyrical prose fuses the drama of *The Bridges of Madison County* with the emotional weight of T*he Notebook* by Nicholas Sparks.
Boston Booksellers

Masterfully written, impressive, highly recommended.
The Midwest Book Review

The intense description of places and emotion is ushered in with beautifully choreographed words that evoke memories and dreams long since buried. What sets Martin apart is the measure of the soul he puts into words, the earthy spirituality too few encounter.
Baltimore Book Reviewer

The depth of connection you feel with the characters is extraordinary. Kirk Martin immerses you into their souls, which makes each page powerful and even life-changing.
Christine Warren

Sometimes life does not grant second chances. Many parents with sick children understand this truth all too well. That's why I am pleased that the Make-A-Wish Foundation®, which grants the wishes of children with life-threatening illnesses to enrich the human experience with hope, strength, and joy, will benefit from the sale of this book.

$1.00 from every purchase of *The Gravel Drive* will be donated to the Make-A-Wish Foundation to help make children's wishes come true.

I appreciate your support and invite you to become involved in this life-changing effort.

For more information about the Make-A-Wish Foundation, visit their website at www.wish.org or call 800-722-9474.

www.kirkmartinbooks.com

I invite you to visit my website:

Receive advance notice of new novels and opportunities to purchase signed copies before they are available in bookstores.

Watch for updates about new titles coming soon!

I am honored that you have chosen to invest your time and resources in this work, and hope that you have found it time well spent. I look forward to sharing more stories with you.